Last Round-Up

Henry Brewis

Farming
Press

For other books by Henry Brewis or a
complete Farming Press catalogue:

www.farmingpress.com
Freephone order line: 08700 780271

Foreword

This book, my final literary fling, was a Farming Press idea really...

"We'd like a sort of cartoon anthology," they said – "a special collection for all that stuff we've published since the far off days of *Funnywayt'mekalivin'*..."

"Well, okay," says I – "sounds an interesting project... as long as the selection is mine. I mean, we can't have some blathering editorial committee debating what politically correct jokes to include, and what to leave out. It might take another millennium to get the thing started..."

"No problem," they said – "get on with it!"

So, a few months later, here we are. A pot-pourri, if you like, of what I consider some of the better cartoons from yesterday, mixed up with a few new ones. A wry, smiley collection to reflect the way farming and the countryside have changed. And, ye gods, the whole scene has certainly changed, hasn't it? Not always for the best.

Which is one reason why farming needs a sense of humour more than ever I think. An ability to laugh at mistakes and disasters. Alright, maybe not just as the ewe drops dead, or the combine develops a terminal cough on a fine day – but hopefully some time later, when the trauma is buried or mended. When your toes are warming by the hearth, and there's a glass of liquid encouragement t'hand. When life has calmed down a bit...
Well, if you can't occasionally see the daftness of it all, and laugh at yourself – you won't survive long as a peasant. You may even require counselling. It was always so.

But I fear it's even harder now. Once it was the normal, traditional calamities that conspired to make farming "exciting". You expected to encounter the dysfunctional sheep, the infuriating collie dog, the broken baler, unreasonable weather, etc. They're still there of course – but so too are the new Eurocrats, the intrusive, bloody-minded bureaucracy, a paper storm of rules and regulations, nosy officials in white coats… and a tidal wave of ill-informed, urban sentimentality, determined to overwhelm the country way of life. Put the peasant in his place – strangle his freedom and independence. It's worrying.

So the hope is that this wee book will conjure up a few therapeutic giggles, chuckles and grins. You may well recognise the odd episode from your own everyday battles, or some character just down the road. I'm certainly in there somewhere.

Then you can put the book in the spare room (especially if you do B&B – it could help enlighten a townie visitor!) Or just leave it lying about in the kitchen. Yes, I reckon it's a kitchen table book, rather than the posh coffee table variety. Anyway, I'm told most of my stuff often ends up in the loo.

Hopefully this book survives long enough to come out of there occasionally.

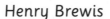

Henry Brewis

First published 2000
Copyright © Farming Press

1 3 5 7 9 10 8 6 4 2

ISBN 0 85236 535 8

A catalogue record for this book is available from the British Library.

Published by Farming Press, Miller Freeman UK Ltd,
Miller Freeman House, Sovereign Way, Tonbridge, Kent TN9 1RW, United Kingdom

Distributed in North America by Diamond Farm Enterprises, Box 537,
Bailey Settlement Road, Alexandria Bay, NY 13607, USA.

Printed by Lavenham Press, Lavenham, Suffolk, UK

I wouldn't worry about the turnout sir – it's a very rural constituency –
no political significance at all really!

That's it – enough – I would go for one of those mega bucks divorce settlements tomorrow –
but half of nowt doesn't come t'much, does it?

You may not believe this missus – but m'very first job as a farm lad
was muckin' out your luxury bedroom…

Well it beats buyin' another lawn mower that's for sure!

Who in their right mind would want to clone one of these crazy things –
why not a nice, dozy Labrador… or a panda… or…

Don't be silly Mother, you've been watching too much television. Anyone would think the countryside was awash with mad cows!

It appears you haven't completed application form AD793/21a subsection 'f' – I'm afraid you'll have to knock it all down again...

Suddenly we seem to be outnumbered Peter. They must breed quicker than us now!

Came to tell me all about rural stress... said he was an expert, an experienced counsellor – and would y'believe it, no sooner had I kicked him out, than sure enough I felt a whole lot better!

I think we can assume the last ewe has lambed and he'll be into his summer ensemble
tomorrow morning...

Sorry Rastas... but if the best you can offer is a quickie and a bright blue backside –
I'm just not impressed...

Nearly ready…

I suspect we may have already exceeded some EU quota dear…

Has anyone ever actually seen a farmer? It could be one of them y'know –
better call security…!

Set off three weeks ago officer – felt we couldn't rely on Mr Prescott's Integrated Transport Plans. All we need now is t'find a decent parkin' space, close to a water trough… and buy a bale o'hay at Harrods maybe…

I'll shift the idle divil… good God, when I was his age…

Y'should've known better – two sheep are no bloody use for a trip like this –
one of them'll drop dead for sure, the first wet night…

No, he's quite alright – it's just that he's allergic to nosy ministry men like you!

SWEEP! Behave yourself!

… and this is the new Trophy Room…

WHOA! Get off m'habitat – don't you realise I'm an endangered
species now – just like you lot…

Well now, the three of you can't be all that wise if you've come all this way
without a reservation...

Oh think nothing of it Mother – he always gets a little stressed at harvest time…
and lambing time… and Christmas time… and IACS time… and…

Come bye t'me y'daft dog – let go and come bye!

Remember the farmer who was so upset just because we had a picnic in his cornfield – well it's him!

Ah, well, Geordie – they did say the showers would be isolated – that's life mate…

I was just going to bury the poor auld thing – but somebody said, hang on, if you had the carcass pickled – she could be a priceless work of art...!

It's on nights like this y'can sympathise with those young hospital doctors who fall asleep on the job, can't y'?

Okay, that's it – this right to roam nonsense has gone too far!

It's the complete tranquillity of the countryside I find so uplifting –
don't you agree Mabel?

We were only seeking a very modest increase Mr Brown –
I do hope we can find a compromise…

"…The hills are alive with the sound of …"

Ssshhh… it's his new mobile phone… fell out of the cab, and he's ploughed it in somewhere. Waiting for someone to ring him, I suppose…

Well, look at it this way dear – forget the snowdrops and the tweeterin' birdies and all that romantic stuff – you and I know this is the first real sign of spring!

They're all leaving – never heard such language at seven in the morning!

Well I told y', didn't I? – You can't have a lie-in just because it's Christmas Day –
it means nowt t'them y'fool!

I'm sure he's in here somewhere Doctor – disappeared three days ago to catch up with some paperwork…

Now if the *News of the World* ever got their hands on a picture of this –
somebody could make a small fortune…

We realise times are difficult – but that bloke will try anything for a bit of sympathy…

That lad from the Job Centre, Charlie… is he any use?

Happens every harvest... forecast's not very good he says... every minute counts he says...
I'll keep it going over dinner time he says...

Hold it Jimmy – I'm not convinced Dad's in the right frame of mind for this…

… and don't look so bloody pleased with yourself – **none** of them are yours, are they?

Townies never understand y'know… if y'just leave Mother Nature to her own devices –
she'll even provide a free lunch for somebody…

Hold on Willie – we seem to have what y'might call a serious wild oat problem here!

I have a feeling we might get a damned good run today Colonel – don't you?

I wouldn't worry – I expect he's hidden away somewhere counting all his subsidies…

Obviously they haven't a clue really… maybe just as well, Sweep and I know
our limitations…

Right then, you happy ramblers – ten seconds before I slip this beast into gear…
one… two… three…

Never mind your glad tidings mate – it'll take another bloody miracle
to get m'sheep back!

Oh dear – we're not in your way are we?

What do y'mean, this is what happens when y'change to organic?
You were always a filthy, smelly, mucky creature…!

Daddy, Teddy wants to know if the combine's not very well today...

Alright, Sweep, we know you're bloody brilliant – BUT NOT NOW!

Well now – could you be the bloke who sent me a rather threatening letter last week…
something about farmers pollutin' the rivers, was it?

Right then – so which one of you budding entrepreneurs sold our tractor
to the scrapman for a fiver and a tube of Smarties?

Just think about it – drugs, sex, violence, foul language, death – it's all around us...
I mean what chance have we got to be normal when we grow up?

Good idea, eh? Saves a whole lot of stress y'know…

It's a clear case of rural rage sergeant – we simply asked him to stop harvesting
for a few hours, so we could observe the mating habits of the Blue Bolivian Aphid –
and he suddenly became very agitated!

So will we have this much fun every time mother has a night out with the girls, Dad?

Now stop that nonsense William – or you'll grow up t'be bad tempered
and destitute like your father…

That was next door inviting us over for supper. He must've finished his combining…

Listen here y'lyin' toad – your cheque is definitely NOT in the post!

Well, I don't mind tellin' y' Peter – I didn't expect to find any of these things here…

I don't think Joseph is entirely convinced about all this...

... and there are those who still make a fuss about being a single parent y'know...

I suppose they must be the ones I promised to pay as soon as we finished the harvest. Didn't expect them all on the same day though...

For all I care, they can ban the whole bloody pantomime on days like this!

Well everything seems to be in order this time Mr Turnbull – no nasty surprises…

Yes – and may the blessings of a bountiful New Year be with you too Vicar…

What y'mean, you've had a rough night – you only have one a year!

Come bye y'randy little bugger – you're not concentratin' are you?

Oh stop sulking – he'll help you with your IACS when he's finished his homework…

Go on Sweep – you tell 'er! Give 'er hell! We've been thoroughly embarrassed
by that yow!

So who have we got here – the man from MLC, two Health and Safety, one Trading Standards, the RSPCA fella… and that dealer from Barnsley – not very promising is it?

I hope you got something nice for the supper dear...

So do I take it Mr Thompson that you don't altogether share my optimism –
not entirely convinced by my imaginative farm expansion plans?

Nothing too outrageous Sharon – something like… charming, idyllic, enormous potential, secluded rural retreat, mature gardens, stunning views, heavenly hideaway… the normal nonsense will do nicely…

Don't be ridiculous – that won't work... she's been dead since last Tuesday!

… and we're very lucky today – a fleeting glimpse of what is rapidly becoming an extremely rare creature – the merry peasant off to work on his bike…

… and I get the impression the lambin's not going too well either…

Maybe we should invite them under cover George – I fear the poor little agitators might perish on a day like this...

Doesn't seem to matter what system we use Mr Johnson – I'm afraid you're still knackered!

… and you reckon that's m'dad. I find it very hard to believe, Mother –
are you absolutely sure?

… actually, he's been in a remarkably good mood lately – but, of course, that can all change in a twinkling of an eye…

It was touch and go for a while, but he's out of danger now – we eventually
found a barley awn drawn over his belly button. Very nasty…

You don't imagine he'll take much notice of you, do you – not after your language in the sheep pens this morning…

C'mon y'great wimp – m'hands aren't that bloody cold!

I realise you think very highly of that dog – but is it possible you've got him
a wee bit spoilt?

Don't be daft man – they'll just be EU spies checkin' up on your oil seed rape acreage!

Get out of here y'smelly old thing – until you've had a bath, this room will be designated a Less Favoured Area!

Actually, I'd appreciate it if you didn't fill it in 'til after the lambin'…

I'm a worried man Doctor – I reckon it's got to be staggers – we have a couple of old yows lookin' very similar…

Okay, we'd better get started – it's a Bank Holiday so the townies'll be out before long, blockin' the roads, bumper to bumper…

Believe me Gladys, the good old days are gone… everybody's lookin' for new ideas –
I think it's called diversification…

Wake up y'fool – this is the third night running you've spent mending the
damned combine!

I'm tellin' you guys… this is positively therapeutic… the weird things that can grow on a plot o'set-aside… way out man… blows yer mind clean off all this farmin' business – who needs it?

Just a little further son – then I'll show y'how to persuade this bloody awkward old yow to accept our poor wee orphan lamb…

Here they come, our upwardly mobile children from the big city – and not a peasant
between them. Where did we go wrong, Gladys?

Don't be daft – no five crop mule yow is worth the kiss of life!

… and as Brother William moves among you – those who have claimed four tonnes to the acre, will surely give more generously than last year…

Well the missus ended up with five solicitors, seven accountants, eleven bank managers, ten school teachers, five plumbers and a couple o' vicars – we thought it was a canny crop really…

For God's sake get your daughter out of the ring Charlie – nobody's interested in your bloody sheep… can't get a bid!

… I think he said he was tidying up the garden today… surprising really, because he never was a keen gardener…

Don't worry Mr Johnson – we'll have your claim sorted out in no time. The village is full of solicitors now!

… and of course all rooms have private facilities…

The sheep nearly got 'im – y'know what the ravenous things are like when they see somebody carryin' a bag…

Okay – so who was foolin' about over the fence last August Bank Holiday
weekend then, eh?

They're usually so damned miserable – I reckon it must be brown envelope time –
in fact I bet they all got their Suckler Cow Premium this morning…

Didn't look much like this in the brochure, Joseph…

Right listen girls – it'll soon be lambing time again and we have to decide who will have the privilege of suddenly dropping dead for no apparent reason!

I don't mind tellin' y'Charlie, she's keeping me now – and I'm not sure whether
I like it or not…

Be gone you worthless lot – this shack is about to be transformed into an executive des res with pony paddock and patio…

There's absolutely nuthin' on my IACS form to stop me harvesting golf balls from the set-aside!

SIT! LIE DOWN! COME BYE!!

What y'makin' all the fuss about – you're on the wrong road anyway!

Okay Sweep – I think we've done our bit for townie relations – put the wee darlin's back on the bus… and don't be frightened to nip a back leg now and then…

Yes, I think we might have found some evidence of a very primitive life form –
but none of us have a clue what it is…

Well sir – he doesn't look like a terrorist...

... and if one of the pathetic things hasn't perished by t'night – I'll certainly
be obliged to sit on one of them before morning...

It's still not too late to dump your impoverished peasant darling – there must
be a nice rich lawyer out there somewhere…

The pathetic price you're offerin' me… I need every last penny… and the wife reckons there's half a tonne like this on the bedroom floor – what's it worth?

Yes, I know pet, but it's hardly worth it – I'll just have to put everything back on again in a couple of hours when I check the lambin' shed!

This is the life eh, Tommy – beats farmin' any day – I don't owe anybody anything now...